Name: _____

Form: _____

Energy Resources

- Read, engage and learn!

- Full colour, illustrated topic booklet.

- Glossary, Memory Map, Active Revision Game, Flashcards.

- Ideal for ISEB 13+ Common Entrance and KS3 pupils.

This Oaka™ Books Write Your Own Notes Booklet goes hand in hand with the Active Learning Pack on this topic. The pack includes a Topic Booklet, an Active Learning Game and Question & Answer flashcards.

Fresh Focus on Learning

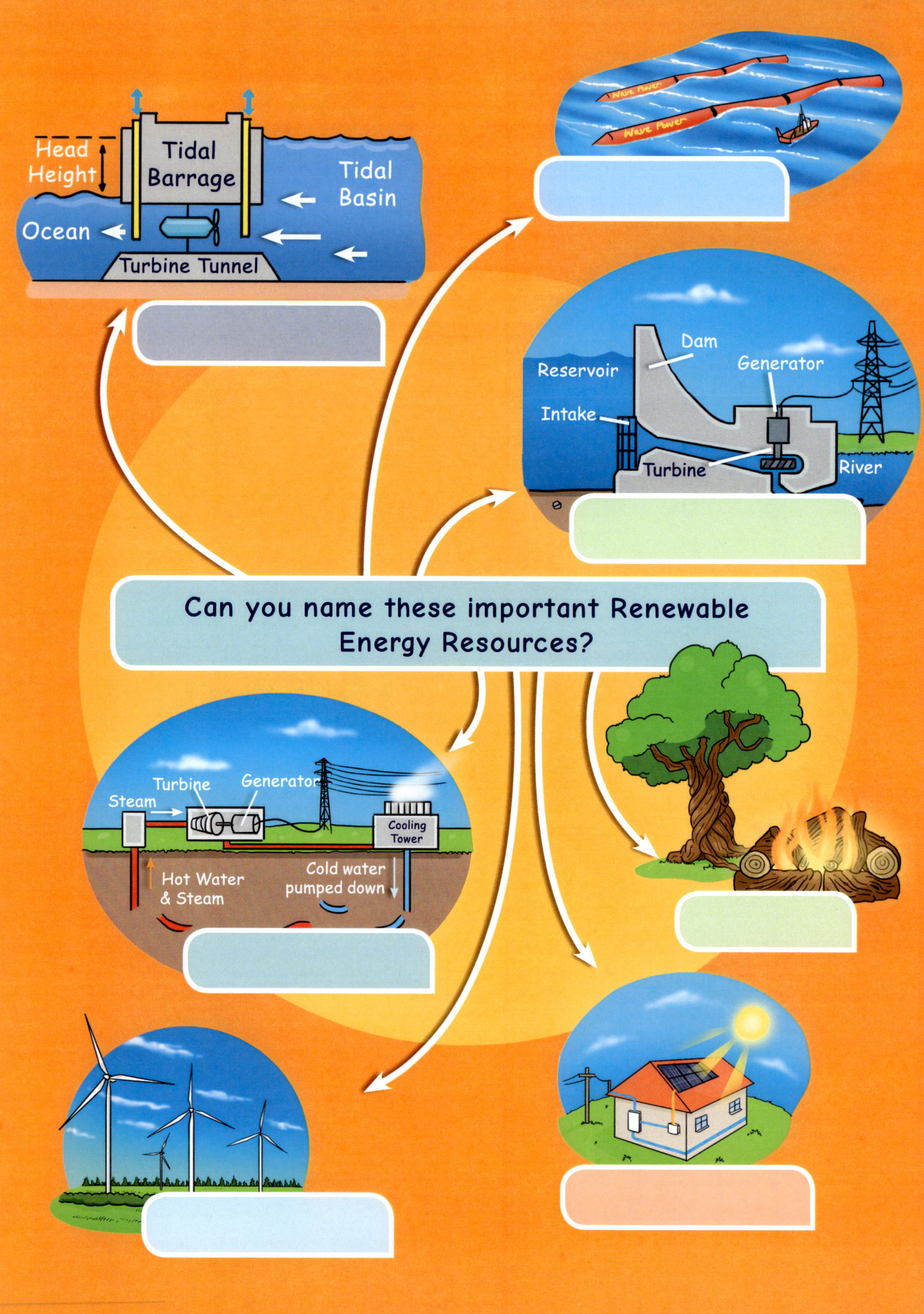

Energy Resources Glossary

Biomass: ....
....
....
....

Fossil: ....
....
....
....

Bunsen: ....
....
....
....

Generator: ....
....
....
....

Burn: ....
....
....
....

Geothermal: ....
....
....
....

Coal: ....
....
....
....

Hydro: ....
....
....
....

Conservation: ....
Save It! ....
....
....

Kinetic Energy: ....
....
....
....

DC/AC: ....
....
....
....

Methane: ....
....
....
....

Electrical: ....
....
....
....

Nuclear: ....
....
....
....

Energy: ....
....
....
....

Oil: ....
....
....
....

Flammable: ....
....
....
....

Oxygen: ....
....
....
....

Energy Resources Glossary

Photosynthesis: ....
....
....
....

Solar: ....
....
....
....

Photovoltaic Cell: ....
....
....
....

Sedimentary Rock: ....
....
....
....

Plutonium: ....
....
....
....

Tidal: ....
....
....
....

Radiation: ....
....
....
....

Transfer: ....
....
....
....

Radio Active: ....
....
....
....

Turbine: ....
....
....
....

Renewable Energy: ....
....
....
....

Uranium: ....
....
....
....

Resource: ....
....
....
....

Wave: ....
....
....
....

Law of Conservation Energy

....
....
....
....

1   Fuels

- Fuels are materials that we .... to release ....

- Fuels give us ...., **thermal** and .... (movement) **energy**.

.... Energy

.... Energy

.... Energy

2   Useful Energy

- But when we use energy (doing work) the .... is always .... out.

- This makes some of it less ....

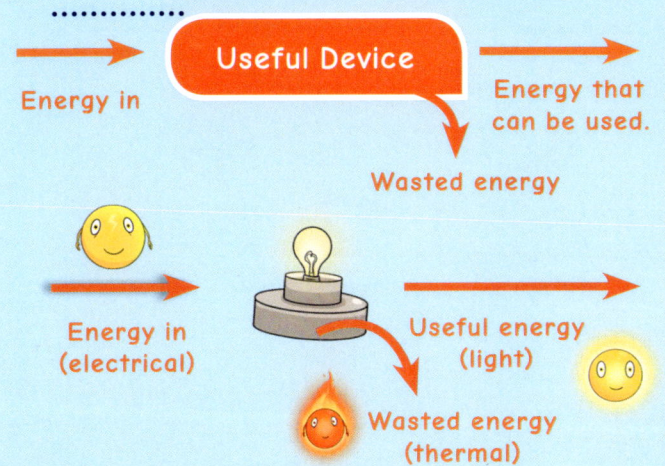

Energy in

Useful Device

Energy that can be used.

Wasted energy

Energy in (electrical)

Useful energy (light)

Wasted energy (thermal)

3   Energy is Transferred in Many Ways

- Plants trap .... from the sun when they make their food by ....

- Animals eat plants and use some of the .... trapped in the ....

- The .... trapped in trees is also released when we .... them.

1

4 Chemical Energy in Fuel

- The **energy** trapped in fuels, like **coal**, is called ....

- When we .... fuels the .... is **turned into thermal** and **light** energy.

.... Contains   ....
....

5 Chemical Energy in Food

- Food is also a fuel that contains ....

- We eat food. The **chemical energy** in the food is **converted into thermal** and ....

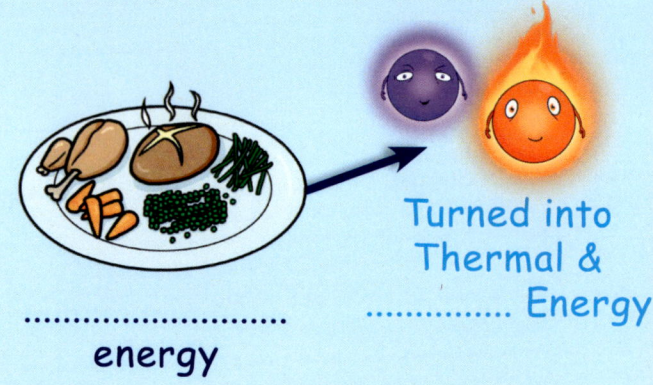

.... energy   Turned into Thermal & .... Energy

6 .... Energy in a Battery

- Batteries also contain .... energy

- The .... **energy** in a battery may be .... **into electrical, thermal, light, kinetic** or ....

Batteries   contain   ....
energy

7 Chemical Energy Transfer

- A torch **transfers**... chemical energy → .... & thermal energy.

electrical

- A radio **transfers**... .... energy → sound energy.

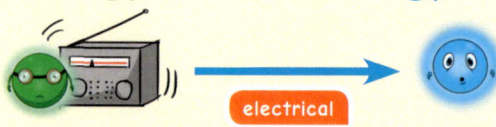
electrical

- A train set **transfers**... chemical energy → kinetic, ... and ....

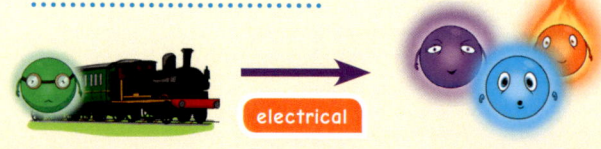
electrical

2

Words to help you...

fossil   non-renewable   renewable   natural gas

nuclear   oil   living things   coal   replaced

---

8   Energy Resources

- **Energy Resources** can be divided into two groups...

1. ....

2. ....

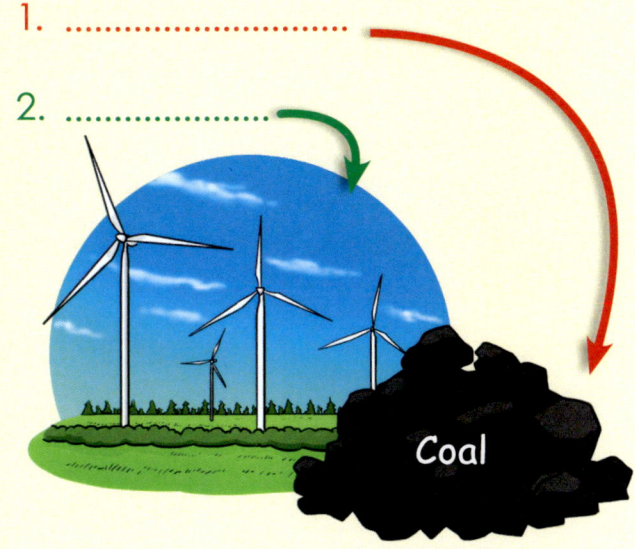

Coal

---

9   Non-Renewable

- .... energy **resources cannot** be ....

- ...., ..., ... and .... are examples of **non-renewable energy resources**.

---

10   Fossil Fuels

- **Coal**, **oil** and **natural gas** are .... fuels.

- They were made from the **remains of** .... that died millions of years ago.

---

11   Fossil Fuels

- The world will **run out** of .... **fuels**.

- .... **fuels** cannot be made again. They are non-........................

Natural Gas

Coal

Oil

12   How is Coal Made?

- The .... is the source of most of the Earth's .... resources.

- **Coal** is made from dead ....

- The plants contain the .... from the .... This is trapped as they make their food by ....

1. Millions of years ago, many giant .... died in ....

Rocks and Dirt

Coal

Rocks and Dirt

3. .... and pressure turned the dead plants into ....

2. The dead plants were buried by ....

13   How is Oil Made?

- **Oil** is made from .... **and** .... that died in the **oceans**.

- The plants contain the **energy** from the ...., trapped as they made their food by ....

- The .... contain the .... from the food that they have eaten.

- The .... and animals were buried by mud and sand .... of years ago.

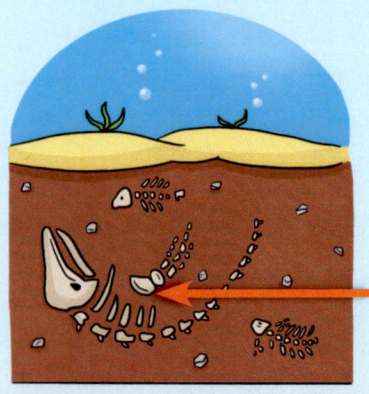

Contains
....
....
from food.

14   How is Natural Gas Made?

- Natural .... is made in the same way as ....

- Natural gas and .... deposits are found **together** under the ....

Dead organisms, plants & animals

.... rocks

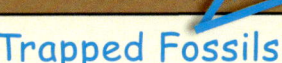

Trapped Fossils

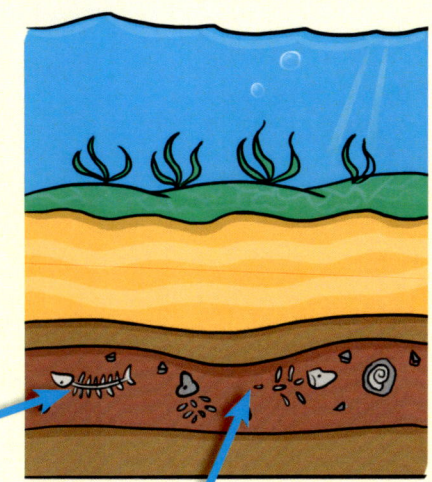

.... rocks

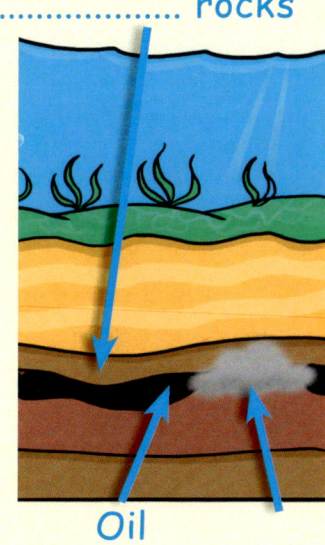

Oil   ....

15   Making Fossil Fuels

- The dead .... and ...., need to be .... before they can rot away.

- They have to be .... under millions of tonnes of dirt, mud and sand.

16   High Pressure

- This causes high .... and **temperature**.

- The dead plants and animals become .... fuels.

- This takes millions of years!

- The **energy** in .... **fuels** first came from the ....!

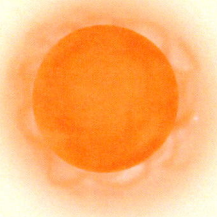

5

17   Renewable Energy

- .... energy **resources** will not run out.

- They will be renewed by the .... energy.

18   Saving Fossil Fuels

- We need to use more ....
.... **resources** to **save** the
...............fuels that we have left.

Fossil fuels will run out!

19   Biomass

- Plants are a good source of .... energy.

- Plants can be grown to be used as fuels. We call this ....

20   Biofuels

- Plants, like sugar cane, can be used as a .... for cars.

- Sugar cane is used as a ....
for ....
They turn the sugar cane into
....

- The **alcohol** is used instead of ....

21   Wind Energy

- The .... in the wind can be used to turn big .... on wind farms.

- .... is **transferred** as **kinetic** (movement) **energy**.

- The **kinetic energy** is used to turn **generators**. These convert .... energy into .... energy.

22   Wave Energy

- Big floats bob up and down as the waves go by.

- The .... **energy** of the floats is used to turn ....

- The **kinetic energy** is used to turn **generators**. These convert .... energy into .... energy.

23   Tidal Energy

- ....energy uses the movement of water to **generate** .... energy.

- As the .... **rises**, water is .... in rivers by **tidal** barrages.

- When the .... **falls**, the water flows over the ....

- The **kinetic energy** of the water turns the ....

- The turbines are connected to **generators**. These convert .... energy into .... energy.

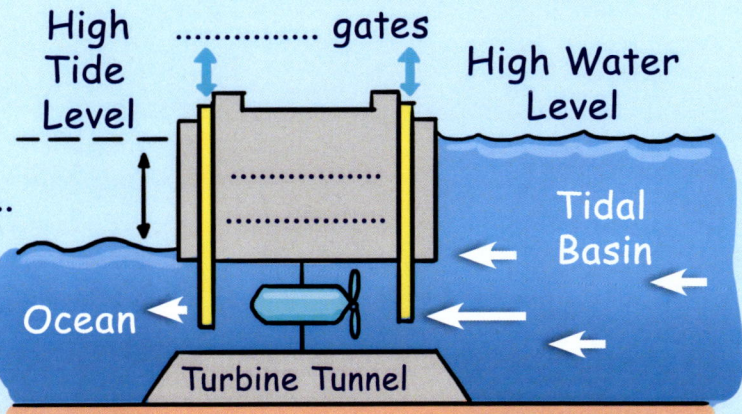

High Tide Level   .... gates   High Water Level

Ocean   Tidal Basin   Turbine Tunnel

Words to help you...

sunlight   photovoltaic cells   solar panel   solar energy
hydro power   turbines   Sun   solar   renewable
radiated   electrical   kinetic   dam

24   Hydro Electric Energy

- .... uses the energy in **flowing water** to make electricity.

- Water is trapped up high, behind a ....

- When the water is **released**, it **flows** over ....

- The .... energy of the water turns the ....

- These are connected to **generators**. These convert .... energy into .... energy.

- .... produces more **energy** than any other source of .... **energy** in the world.

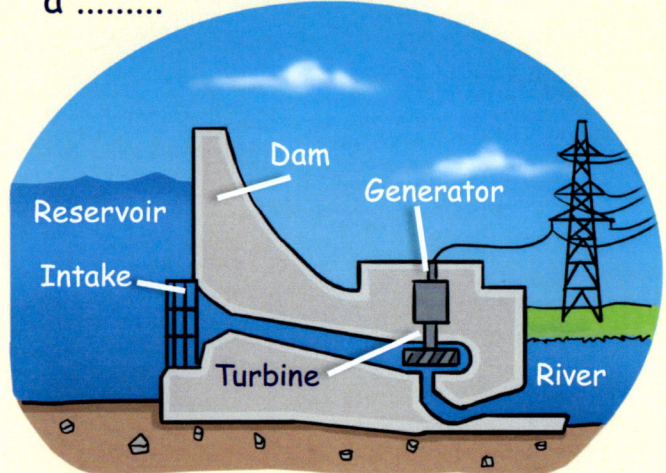

Reservoir
Intake
Dam
Generator
Turbine
River

25   Energy from Sunlight

- **Energy** from the .... is called .... **power**.

- The **energy** from the .... is .... to the earth.

- Plants use .... to make food by photosythesis.

.... on roof turns
sunlight into DC current

Extra electricity
is saved on grid

....
turn DC to AC

8

Words to help you...

non-renewable   nuclear energy   radioactive   turbines
electrical   kinetic   underground   boils   geothermal
steam   Plutonium   pressure   electricity   cold

26 Geothermal Energy

- .... is using the heat from deep **underground** to heat water.

- It can be used to make .... or heat homes.

- .... water is pumped **down**. It .... and comes back up as ....

- The **high** .... of the steam **turns** the ....

- These are connected to **generators**. These convert .... energy into .... energy.

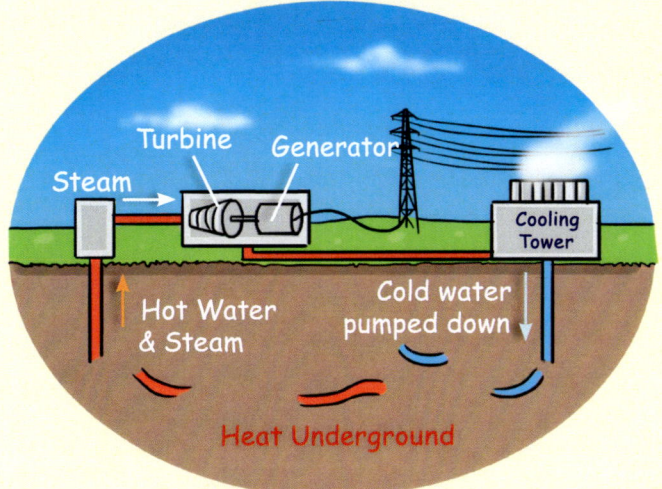

Steam

Turbine   Generator

Cooling Tower

Hot Water & Steam

Cold water pumped down

Heat Underground

27 Non-Renewable Nuclear

- Some chemical elements, like .... and **Uranium**, are ....

- When their atoms **break down**, they give out ....

- The nuclear energy can be used to turn water into .... to turn ....

- .... produces harmful **nuclear waste** that can last for hundreds of years.

- **Nuclear** is classed as ....

9

Words to help you...

chemical   electrical energy   transfer   steam   water
fuels   joule   solar energy   plants   energy   animals   thermal
sound   Earth's   electricity   electrical   oxygen   biomass

28   Using Fuels

- Fuels are **flammable**. They **burn** in ....

- **Coal, oil, gas,** .... and **nuclear** .... can all be used to **generate** ....

- Power stations use fuels to .... the **chemical energy**, trapped in fuels, into .... energy.

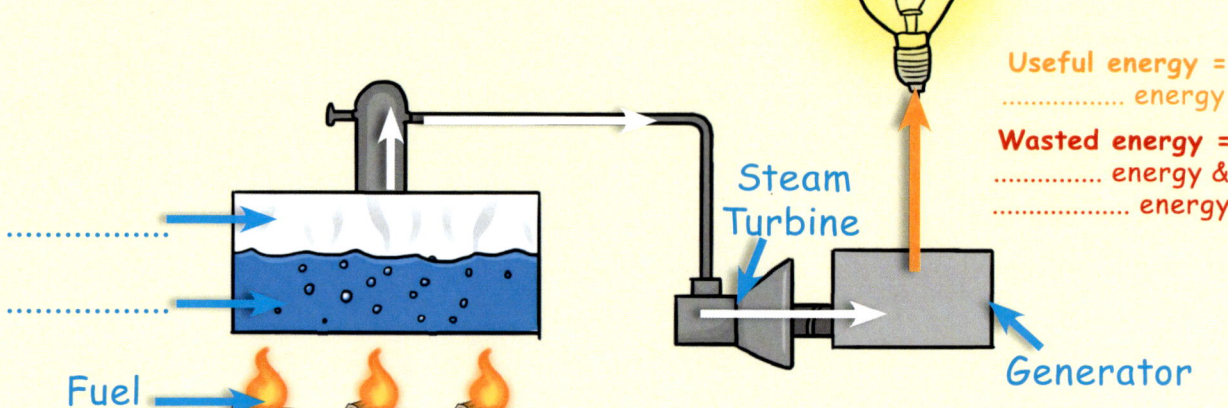

Useful energy = ... energy

Wasted energy = ... energy & .... energy

Steam Turbine

Generator

Fuel

29   Joule

- The .... is the unit that we use to measure **energy**.

- The .... is a very small unit.

- It would take you 1 .... of **energy** to lift an apple 1 metre into the air.

30   Things to Remember About Sunlight

- The Sun is the .... source of nearly all the .... **energy resources**.

- Plants trap .... during photosynthesis.

- .... are at the beginning of all food chains. Animals eat .... and we eat plants and animals.

- Food (.................. energy) is the .... source for ....

Do you know how fossil fuels were made?

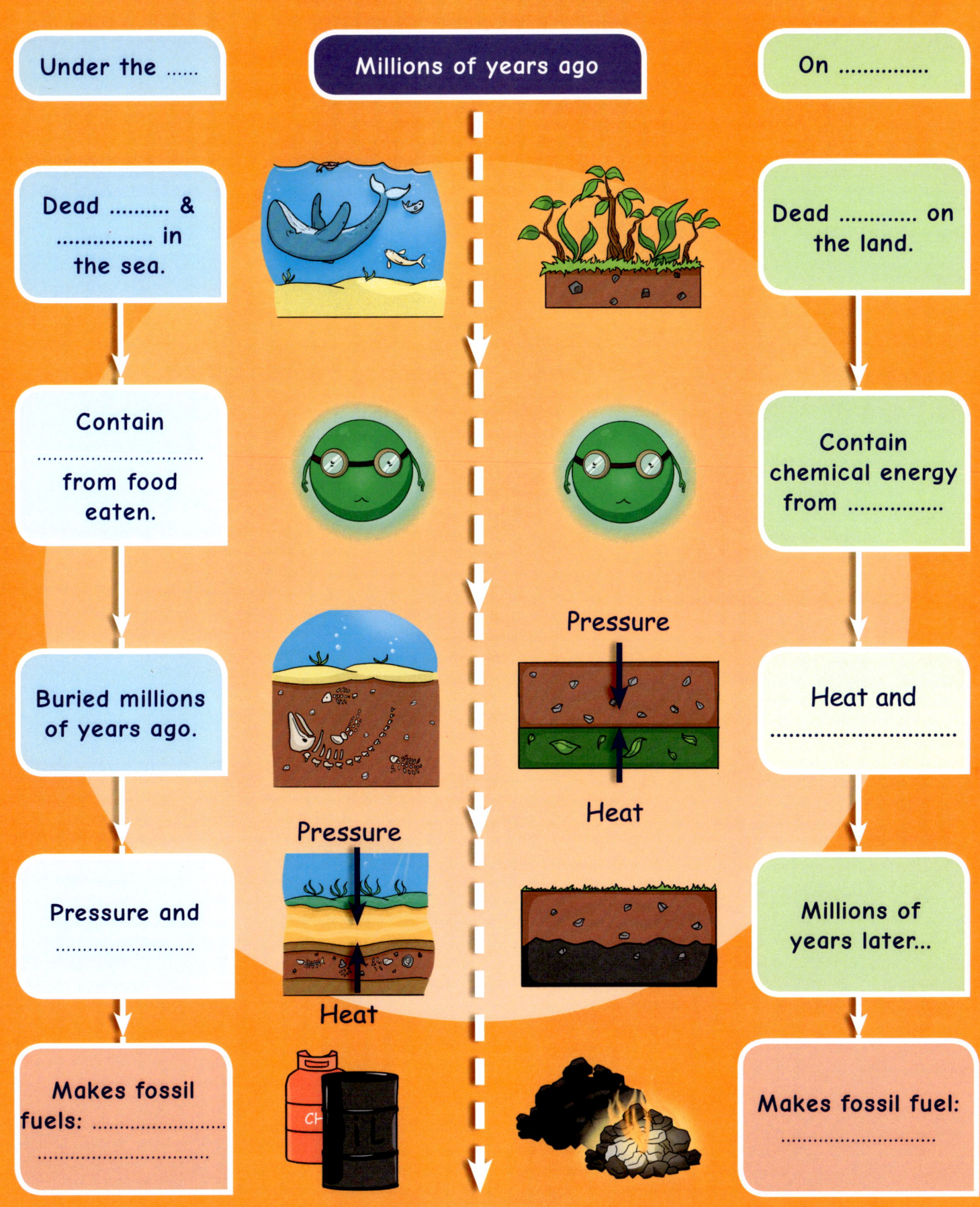

Under the ......

Dead .... & .... in the sea.

Contain .... from food eaten.

Buried millions of years ago.

Pressure and ....

Makes fossil fuels: ....

Millions of years ago

Pressure

Heat

Pressure

Heat

On ....

Dead .... on the land.

Contain chemical energy from ....

Heat and ....

Millions of years later...

Makes fossil fuel: ....

Today

About Oaka Books

Children learn best when they are engaged...

Our aim is to help children enjoy learning by making it fun! That way they will succeed.

Following ISEB 13+ Common Entrance and National Curriculum guidelines for KS3.

Design and layout of our books follow guidelines from the British Dyslexia Association.

Three Easy Steps

Read: the easy to follow bullet point Topic Booklet.

Engage: Play the Active Learning Game.

Learn: When you understand the topic, test yourself using the Write Your Own Notes Book. You can use the Topic Booklet to help if you get stuck.

One (short) Topic at a time:

For some students, a big book is a big turn off. That's why we focus on one topic at a time. Short and to the point.

Reading Age

This booklet is suitable for children with a reading age of 10 ½ years.

Topic Packs for KS1, KS2 & KS3 Include:

History
Geography
Chemistry
Biology
Physics

Please visit www.oakabooks.co.uk for more information about forthcoming titles.

First paperback edition printed 2015 in the United Kingdom.
A catalogue record for this book is available from the British Library.

ISBN 978-1-909892-63-7

Designed, set and published by Oaka™ Books.

To order other titles from Oaka™ Books, please email info@oakabooks.co.uk or visit www.oakabooks.co.uk, or phone: +44 (0) 2392 388519.

Acknowledgements
Our huge thanks go to the many teachers who have been involved in the development of this series of learning guides. Special thanks to Joy Gardiner, for producing hundreds of illustrations, to Kate Doehren, for her enthusiasm and invaluable assistance to my wonderful daughter Sophie, for being the inspiration for the books and, of course, to Charlie, for believing in them.

ISBN 978-1-911189-88-6

CE/KS3
Energy Resources
Write Your Own Notes Booklet